Called to Serve: The Minister in the Making
A Roadmap to Ministerial Training

Companion Workbook

Copyright © 2020 by Dr. Doretha D. Allen
Publisher: Smarti Designs, LLC

Scripture quotations are from THE LIFE IN THE SPIRIT STUDY BIBLE, KING JAMES VERSION. Copyright 1992, 2003 by the Zondervan Corporation. Grand Rapids, Michigan

Scripture Quotations are from THE MESSAGE: THE BIBLE IN CONTEMPORARY LANGUAGE, Large Print Numbered Edition
Copyright 2002 by Eugene H. Petersen

Printed in the United States of America

Cover Art: Public Domain

Table of Contents

Concepts
- The textbook and work book together is a unique manual for the training and deploying of leaders in the kingdom of God.

- Small Bible study groups along with home study groups will find this a helpful tool in assisting them with their training of potential leaders.

- This workbook will be a helpful resource for individual study.

- Individuals will also be able draw from the chapters that best suit their particular needs.

- This training workbook will help you to determine where you are in ministry.

Directions:
1. Read the chapters thoroughly in the textbook before beginning.

2. If there are questions, revisit the information in the chapter before making your final decision.

3. If you are reading this book as a small group, your group leader will make sure there is consensus before moving to the next question.

4. Notice that some questions ask for your individual response.

5. Keep a Bible and other study aids nearby.

6. Get Started!

Questions

1. It is a necessary and supernatural vocation; being a _____ instituted by God and vital to man's eternal condition.

2. The truth is, according to the Bible, every person that hears the gospel is called, because the _____ _____ is a call to salvation.

3. Just before beginning the celebration of their feast days, the priests were assigned the _____ of sounding the trumpets.

4. In I Corinthians 7:21, "called" is almost equivalent to "_____" which points to the moment when faith was born.

5. It would probably not be biblically inappropriate to extend the idea of _____ to all ministries within the church.

6. It is the "_____" or invitation to salvation that carries the weight of the New Testament definition because a person cannot be called to the _____ of ordained ministry without first being summoned to salvation.

7. Ministry's aim is to inspire you for individual _____ and not _____.

8. The information compiled in this book is intended to bring _____ to the biblical words of "call and _____."

9. Simply stated, ministers, whether dressed in pompous attire or layman's garb are all called to _____.

10. Some biblical terms have taken on meaning that reflect the post Christian Era, _____ and denominational _____.

11. For the aspiring minister, nothing can be more important than a _____ _____ with Jesus Christ.

12. The _____ of ministry must be aligned with God's purpose.

13. Regardless of _____ or _____, every Christian will be rewarded according to their work.

14. The models that every aspiring ministry should _____ in order to understand what the requirements of ministry are can be found in the Bible.

15. This workbook is intentionally geared towards those who seek to be properly _____ for the work of ministry as the Bible instructs.

16. As you may already be aware, God approved ministerial workplaces _____ on your daily life.

17. We have discussed that ministry regardless of the task, demands that a person be _____ oriented.

18. The minister must be prepared for _____, both pleasant and unpleasant.

19. Stationed in a posture of service the minister has the opportunity to view life from a _____ view.

20. God has a discipleship pathway that is a _____ process that will move you steadily along the pathway of ministry.

21. You will come to realize that the fulfillment of the _____ _____ is at the core of all acts of ministry.

22. This manual is designed to make your study _____ and meaningful while focusing on key areas of ministerial pursuits.

23. Only God through the Holy Spirit can ultimately impart to you the
_____ _____ and _____
_____needed in order to be what he has ordained you to be.

24. The information shared with you in this workbook will hopefully convince you that ministry is a _____ _____ and a profession invented by man.

25. Write out Titus 1:5-9

_____

_____

_____

26. What are some leadership requirements Paul listed in II Timothy 3 and Titus 2

_____

_____

_____

_____

Reflections: Use the space below to express your thoughts after considering the above-mentioned questions.

Chapter One
Prerequisites to Ministry

Questions

1. What does the word "prerequisite" mean?

    _____

    _____

    _____

    _____

2. Why do companies have company policies in place for the new employee?

    _____

    _____

    _____

    _____

3. A new believer is like a new employee in that both must perform at a high

    _____.

4. It is the unfailing and biblically modeled _____ that God has already put in place that makes us ready for ministry.

5. Ministry is a _____ calling.

6. What does "regeneration" mean? _____.

7. The _____ _____ disciples lasted for three and a half years under the direct supervision of Jesus.

8. Compare the steps in building a house to those of building a ministry.

    A ministry   A House

    _____   _____

    _____   _____

    _____   _____

    _____   _____

    _____   _____

9. Why must shortcuts never to be taken in ministry?

_____

_____

10. Name the fruit of the spirit.

    A. _____

    B. _____

    C. _____

    D. _____

    E. _____

    F. _____

    G. _____

    H. _____

    I. _____

11. How does "compassion" differ from love?

_____

_____

12. What does "humility" mean?

_____

_____

13. The requirement of the _____ _____and the _____ of the Holy Ghost are the first_____ _____for Christian Ministry.

14. What is the meaning of Peace? _____.

15. _____ is defined as state of quietness, rest, repose, harmony; order in midst of turmoil.

16. Goodness is the state of being good, _____, _____.

17. The underlying stages of construction that makes a house beautiful, is similar to ministry in that the _____of the spirit are hidden from view.

18. For _____ and _____ that pertain to God's process of ministry, the _____ should always be our _____ _____ _____.

19. What does I Corinthians 15:58 state?

_____

_____

_____

20. What should our lives reveal _____ virtues of _____ and all _____?

21. What should we as Christians give attention to?

_____

_____

22. What must the newcomer do? _____ submit to being _____ and _____ by persons assigned to that duty.

23. The student must be? _____

24. True or False. The student must be filled with the Spirit of God?

_____

25. True or False. The minister must wait to be deployed by the Church.

_____

Reflections: Record your thoughts from chapter one. What did you learn?

Chapter Two
The Minister in the Making

Questions

1. The development of leader takes place _____.

2. Leaders are developed in places like, _____,
   _____, _____, _____,
   _____, _____, _____,
   and _____..

3. All Christians began as putty in God's hands, _____ by sin.

4. The moment we yield ourselves to God, He takes us into His hand. He begins
   to work out His plan to _____ and _____ us
   into the vessel He has already determined us to become.

5. Write Jeremiah 29:11.

   _____
   _____
   _____

6. God prepares each vessel to function without imperfections and
   _____.

7. Becoming the person that God requires a person to be, requires that we go
   through a process that include _____, _____,
   and _____ growth.

8. God starts us off with small responsibilities that require our _____to
   basic principles.

9. Explain this verse of scripture: "…the little foxes, that spoil the vines…"

   _____
   _____
   _____

10. What happened to Adam and Eve as punishment for disobeying God?

   _____
   _____

11. Did Jesus go through a time of preparation before beginning his Ministry? Give proof of your answer by giving the book of the Bible, chapter, and verse.

_____

_____

12. What is the definition of mentoring?

_____

_____

13. What should happen during the mentoring process?

_____

_____

_____

14. Paul advised Timothy to make every effort to avoid the debate of _____ and scientific _____.

15. The aim of a mentor is _____; prophetic in nature.

16. Your mentors will pour into you the same qualities and graces that were emptied into them by their _____.

17. At the Jordan River Elisha asked Elijah for a _____, _____ of his spirit.

18. Jesus chose twelve men from among the common people to become His _____.

19. _____ True or False Timothy's reputation as a reputable young man, eager to learn made him Paul's choice for _____ training.

20. Give four examples of Biblical Mentoring.

    A. _____

    B. _____

    C. _____

    D. _____

21. In what way(s) have you met the qualifications that would make you a good choice for ministry?

Reflections: In your own words discuss the necessity of having an example to learn from when being developed for ministry.

_____

_____

_____

_____

_____

_____

_____

_____

_____

_____

_____

_____

_____

_____

_____

_____

_____

_____

_____

_____

Chapter Three
Does the Collar Qualify?

Questions

1. Every person that is born into the world is born into a world _____ by sin.

2. What does the Bible reveal about the words, "minister" and "ministry?"

   _____

   _____

   _____

3. According to the Bible a minister is one that

   _____A. attends, serve, waits on

   _____B. helps

   _____C. was created by God

   _____D. all of the above

4. Which Hebrew word for minister means to serve, or do service for?

   _____A. diakonos

   _____B. sarat

   _____C. kahan

   _____D. All of the above

5. In the Biblical context, the word _____ meant having the skills necessary for the successful completion of a task.

6. Many envision _____ as the opportunity to wear elegant attire and have others serve them.

7. The person with a _____ heart does not seek to be _____ .

8. The heart of a servant is not preoccupied with having _____ desires satisfied.

9. According to Jesus the person that declares himself to be greatest should position himself to render the _____ service.

10. Give one example of an unselfish act performed by Christ.

_____

_____

_____

11. The proper functioning of_____ is service, and we must embrace this truth if the Church is going to complete her _____ in the world.

12. A call into ministry is a call for _____, _____, and investors.

13. Ministry equates to Christian acts of _____ in the area of missions and evangelism.

14. A strong, healthy, resilient body was necessary to carry the work of the _____ _____ priest.

15. Believers have a two-way ministry, in the direction of the _____ and in the direction of the _____.

16. Compare and contrast some differences between the duties of Old Testament priests and what New Testament ministers are expected to do.

Old Testament Priests	New Testament Priests
_____	_____
_____	_____
_____	_____
_____	_____

17. The New Testament call is a _____ to serve others.

18. God is waiting for _____ vessels. People that are _____ to the order of the kingdom.

19. Our understanding of man being made in the image of God should clarify our doubts regarding the role of _____.

20. Though the duties of ministry have evolved over time, the _____ of service to others runs throughout the Bible.

Journaling: Write a summary of the following three words, comparing and contrasting.

Sarat

Kahan

Diakonos

Chapter Four
Laborers Needed

Questions

1. What does the scripture mean by "repent" the kingdom of heaven is at hand.

   _____
   _____
   _____

2. Why was Jesus moved with compassion when He looked out over the multitude in Saint Matthew 9:36-37?

   _____
   _____
   _____

3. The priests had lived among human squalor for long, they became _____ to its presence.

4. Jesus made the _____ not only responsible to spread the gospel, but to give aid, whenever possible, to citizens of their community.

5. As the first members of the New Testament Church, the disciples were the _____ by which all ministers after them would be defined.

6. Harvest means

   _____A. mental effort

   _____B. employed workers

   _____C. to pluck, gather, the season for gathering in agricultural crops

7. A laborer is _____.

8. Whenever there is _____, there no danger of the fruit ruining on the vine.

   _____A. plenteous workers

   _____B. laborers

   _____C. friends

9. Why do so many available disciples stand idle waiting for some one else to do the field work?

      A. Because they feel that can choose what they want to do

      B. Because there is no glamour in field work

      C. Both A & B

10. Jesus' desire for permanent workers was based on the fact that _____ workers know that they are working only temporary and would not put forth their best effort.

11. Many a person called into ministry has begun with great _____ but when the duty became _____ they failed to remain diligent.

12. Everyone of the disciples were promoted to apostleship except _____.

13. Jesus is looking for workers who are _____.

      A. Faithful

      B. Obstinate

      C. Contrary

14. Jesus' call is universal but _____ are chosen.

      A. Many

      B. Few

      C. 80%

15. Write Isaiah 6:8

_____

_____

_____

16. Gleaning is a task that calls for a group of people that is aware that the work is _____ .

17. The job of harvesting must done expeditiously, but _____.

18. Does it matter if you are called to work in the field or barn? Why?

_____
_____
_____

19. Write Revelation 22:12.

_____
_____
_____
_____
_____
_____

20. Jesus put the Kingdom of God on display through _____ of service.

Journaling: What are your after thoughts after completing the questions?

Chapter Five
Areas of Opportunity

Questions

1. Research says there are approximately _____ people on earth. Why is this important to the minister?

   _____

   _____

   _____

2. Copy I Corinthian 12:18?

   _____

   _____

   _____

3. When comparing the parts of the body to the Body of Christ, Paul declared that each has a particular _____ to perform.

4. God's choice of your ministry is based on his knowledge of your spiritual _____ _____, and skills.

5. When assigning ministry God already knows where you _____ best.

6. Paul felt that the New Testament Christian could better understand ministry through the _____, positioning and functioning of the parts of the human body.

7. Paul explained that there are _____ of gifts and different administrations.

8. The entire Church must function as a _____ to support and strengthen the body.

9. The _____ ministry of the apostle, prophet, evangelist, pastor, and teacher is the strong leadership that God has put in place to prepare the Church as a whole.

10. The team that God has gifted to assist or undergird five-fold ministry is called the ministry of _____.

11. Each member needs the support of the other for the purpose of _____ and proper growth.

12. Lay ministry is the work provided by those in the Church who are not considered to be _____ clergy.

13. Regardless of position, we all must serve in some _____ before being promoted to a place of leadership.

14. Name five positions of lay ministry where service is needed.

    A._____

    B._____

    C._____

    D._____

    E._____

15. What does Saint Matthew 23:14 say?

_____

_____

_____

16. _____ Ministry is a term used to describe the religious leadership obtained through formal training within a church denomination.

17. Professional clergymen usually hold a _____ degree in particular field of religious study and have been ordained.

18. What each person who comes to Christ should be striving for is the spiritual target of _____.

19. Name five examples of professional ministry.

    A._____

    B._____

    C._____

    D._____

    E._____

20. Jesus' followers were all common people from the _____,
    _____ and _____ of Galilee.

21. _____ True or False   Since Jesus' disciples were not trained in a classroom
    and they turned out well, we should not be trained either.

22. _____ of study and acceptance of Biblical ignorance should never
    be replaced by some type of training be it formal or informal.

23. Nicodemus confessed that the leaders of the Great Sanhedrin knew that Jesus
    was a _____ come from God.

24. Daniel prophesied that the time would come when men from various areas
    would interact with each other and _____ would increase.

25. Write I Peter 3:15.

    _____

    _____

    _____

    _____

Journaling. Write down your thoughts on Chapter Five.

Chapter Six
On Stage or Behind the Curtains

Questions

1. Ministry that is done quietly, that operates from a concealed position is called _____ the scenes ministry.

2. Paul compared the parts and systems of the _____ body to the Body of Christ for a better understanding of how no one part is more important than the other.

3. Paul taught that the number of parts that operate from behind the scenes are _____ in quantity.

4. Just as the success of actors on stage is due to the design, _____ and proper placement of stage props, the Body of Christ functions because of work done by _____ ministry.

5. Without the _____ system the arms and legs would move.

6. Like the inner body parts, the work that the lay members do cannot be seen, therefore tend to receive less _____.

7. When it comes to the natural body, the _____ organs drive the systems of the body to insure proper function.

8. Like the natural body, each member of the Body of Christ works for the good of all. _____ True _____ False

9. Each member of the Body of Christ are interdependent-working for the whole body. _____ True _____ False

10. The anatomy of the human body reveals that _____ between organs do not exist because each has a God ordained. _____

11. The Circulatory System is responsible for

    _____A. Digestion and processing food

    _____B. Pumping and channeling blood to and from the body and lungs

    _____C. Providing Muscular Movement

12. The Nervous System is responsible for

    _____A. Communication with the body using hormones

    _____B. Providing the muscles with movement

    _____C. Collecting, transferring and processing information with the brain

13. The Urinary System is responsible for

    _____A. Kidneys, ureters, bladders, etc.

    _____B. Maintain the body's temperature

    _____C. Breathing

14. List the ten most vital organs

    A._____

    B._____

    C._____

    D._____

    E._____

    F._____

    G._____

    H._____

    I ._____

    J._____

15. Paul used the members of the body to show us that we should never assign _____ of importance to ministry gifts.

16. Just as every member of the body is needed, so is every member of the Body of Christ. If one part is _____ the body does not function at its best.

17. The members of the Body of Christ _____ as a team just as the members of the body.

18. We receive our giftedness from God. He knows where
    we are best suited to serve. _____ True _____ False

19. "Behold, I come quickly, my _____ is with me, to give to every
    man according to what his work shall be."

20. Your _____ will be realized as you successfully carry out your duties
    from your assigned place.

21. God gives us gifts according to our several _____.

22. The _____ system fights off disease.

    _____ A. Urinary system

    _____ B. Nervous system

    _____ C. Immune system

23. The _____ are located under the ribcage in your lower back.

    _____ A. Kidneys

    _____ B. Immune system

    _____ C. Nervous system

24. The _____ is located in the abdomen behind the stomach.

    _____ A. Urinary system

    _____ B. Pancreas

    _____ C. Immune system

25. The _____ _____ is located in your abdomen and is 1.5 meters
    in length.

Journaling

Chapter Seven
Make Your Calling and Election Sure

Questions

1. Peter is credible because, he along with the other 12 had been with Jesus and, because of their connection to Jesus had suffered _____ treatment.

2. What are the virtues listed in II Peter chapter five that must be added to our faith.

    A._____

    B._____

    C._____

    D._____

    E._____

    F._____

    G._____

3. God is presently raising an army of men and women to go into all the world as his _____.

4. The three phases of entering the ministry is _____, _____, and _____.

5. It does matter if you have been called to governmental ministry, or to volunteer because the process is not the same. _____True or _____False

6. It does matter if you have been called to full time ministry, or lay ministry because the process and the requirements are not the same. _____ True _____ False

7. God always uses an _____ getter to cause us to take _____.

8. God may also use other _____ of _____ to confirm your calling but they should never replace the voice of God.

9. Which heritage provided Paul with legal protection throughout his ministry?

_____

10. What does making your calling and election sure means?

_____

_____

_____

_____

11. Explain the similarities of the three phases of entering the ministry.

_____

_____

_____

_____

_____

_____

_____

_____

_____

12. Which phase of ministry training are you in?

_____

_____

_____

13. Are you currently being prepared or have you already been sent?
_____ Yes _____ No

14. Jesus ordained his disciples for the task of global _____.

15. Moses was also given time to learn the ways of the _____; to make sure he knew their _____, _____.

Journaling

Chapter Eight
The Ministry Gifts

Questions

1. What are the ministry gifts listed in Ephesians 4:11?

    A. _____

    B._____

    C._____

    D._____

    E._____

2. What are the duties of the Ministry gifts listed in Ephesians four?

    A. _____

    B. _____

    C. _____

    D. _____

    E. _____

    F. _____

    G. _____

    H. _____

3. _____ are those that instruct the Bible in a logical, systematic way so as to communicate information for true understanding and growth.

4. The usage of this gift is an enablement to perform _____ _____ which are acknowledged to be of supernatural origin.

5. How are measures of gifting given to man?

    _____

    _____

    _____

6. What is the difference between the word of wisdom and the word of knowledge?

_____

_____

_____

_____

7. Describe the ministry gifts in Romans Chapter 12.

A. Prophesy _____

_____

B. Ministry _____

_____

C. Teaching _____

_____

D. Exhortation _____

_____

E. Giving _____

_____

F. Rulership _____

_____

G. Mercy _____

_____

Journaling: How does Christ distribute His gifts?

Chapter Nine
Where Do I Fit In?

Questions

1. What does the word "service" mean?

    _____

    _____

2. Discovering your particular ministry gift should be a pleasurable exercise and not a _____.

3. Your _____, _____ and _____ all contribute to knowing where you best fit for ministry.

4. The combination of characteristics or qualities that form an individual's distinctive character is known as _____.

5. Passion is defined as any powerful or compelling emotion. _____ True _____ False

6. Knowing what peaks your interest is one ministry assessment tool that can be used to discover where you best fit in. _____ True _____ False.

7. Preparing the whole person is taking the holistic approach to ministry fitness. _____ True _____ False

8. The gift itself is never more important than knowing how to _____ the gift for the benefit of others.

9. When God placed you in the Body of Christ, He took your _____, _____, and your _____ into consideration.

10. As a _____ of the Body of Christ there is a _____ and place _____ especially with you in mind.

11. Your ministry gift is like pieces that fit in a puzzle. Regardless to how similar the pieces look, none of them can be _____ to fit anywhere else but where it is designed to fit.

12. Passion is _____.

       _____A. Practical contact with and observation of facts or events

       _____B. Any powerful all compelling emotion

       _____C. Qualities that make someone interesting or popular

13. Ministry can be demanding. Take the _____ approach.

14. Your God given talents and abilities are _____ to your gifts.

15. Those that feel most comfortable talking to crowds of people may be given the ministry gift of _____.

16. Seeking to discover your special gift should always be seasoned with

     _____.

17. In the book of Ecclesiastes, Solomon encourages us _____.

       _____A. Whatever you find in your hands to do, do with all your might.

       _____B. Seek the Lord

       _____C. Pray without ceasing

       _____D. Preach sound doctrine

Journaling

Chapter Ten
Ministerial Qualities and the Leadership Role

Questions

1. Many are interpreting the Bible to mean what it does not in order to suit their own desires. _____ True _____ False

2. In what books did Paul lay down the discipline and regulations for church order and the qualifications for various ministries? _____

3. God will not only reward us for our work but also for the _____ of our work and the _____ behind our service.

4. List 10 descriptions of a good minister from Paul list.

   A. _____

   B. _____

   C. _____

   D. _____

   E. _____

   F. _____

   G. _____

   H. _____

   I. _____

   J. _____

5. Paul holds that all _____ are called to live exemplary Christian lives, but _____, especially, are held to a higher standard.

6. The lives of leaders should be set forth as a pattern of living that pleases God. Those seeking leadership in the Church must live consecrated lives. _____ True _____ False

7. What caused the face of the Church to change on the day of Pentecost?

   _____

8. Paul told Timothy to _____ stay with the truth.

9. _____ yourself as a means of personal inspection.

10. "If anyone wants to provide leadership in the church, good! There are no preconditions..." _____ True _____ False

11. What books are known to us as the Pastoral letters?

    _____A. I Timothy, I Corinthians, and Titus

    _____B. I & I Timothy and Titus

    _____C. Colossians, I Timothy, and Titus

12. According to Paul, the character of those that seek leadership in the church is much more important than _____, _____, _____, or academic accomplishments.

13. The conduct of church leaders should always reflect the truth in both word and _____.

Journaling

Chapter Eleven
The Public Sector: All Eyes on You

Questions

1. Remember that you have not been called to a _____ or
   _____. You are called to go and bring forth
   _____.

2. What specific methodology should be used to select and appoint qualified
   spiritual leaders?

   _____

   _____

   _____

   _____

   _____

3. If you are irresponsible as a citizen in your local community, you will be
   irresponsible with the things of God. _____ True _____ False

4. Our words must be the language of the _____.

5. What was Paul explaining to Timothy in I Timothy 4:12?

   _____

   _____

   _____

   _____

   _____

6. The word translated "example" is the Greek word _____ which
   means, pattern, image, model, or ideal.

7. A _____ committed to winning the _____ of men for
   Christ must be _____ in every arena of life.

8. Why did Paul warn Timothy against placing novices or newcomers to the faith in positions of leadership?

_____

_____

_____

_____

_____

_____

9. Who must our character reflect? _____

10. We do not have to be well respected by those in our community in order to minister to them. _____ True _____ False

11. You have been called to cry loud and declare _____, which is not always accepted.

12. The life of a person seeking leadership should not be marred by serious sin, immorality, by habit, or by _____, his life should serve as a model for all to follow.

13. The Word of God acts as a _____, in that it detects the slightest flaw in our character.

Journaling

Chapter Twelve
Principles of Study

Questions

1. Paul advised Timothy to set aside time for _____ because he must be able to _____ up other men to succeed him in ministry.

2. The word "study" comes from the word "orthodox" which means to _____   _____.

3. In order for Timothy to make an _____ on the lives of others, it was a must that he studied to make sure that he was preaching sound _____.

4. Rightly _____ the word has the imagery of a skilled physician carefully _____ a body of its parts.

5. Handling the word right means _____.
   A. Be as accurate as possible
   B. Dissect the word correctly
   C. Study when its convenient
   D. C
   E. Both A & B

6. _____ is the study of the interpretation of the books of the Bible.

7. The study of the composition and delivery of a sermon is _____.
   A. Exegesis
   B. Homiletics
   C. Hermeneutics

8. The "cutting out" of a text is known as _____.
   A. Homiletics
   B. Exegesis
   C. Eisegesis

9. _____ is reading into the text what is not there.

10. What are some questions to consider when doing a hermeneutical study of a book or chapter?

A. _____

B. _____

C. _____

D. _____

E. _____

F. _____

G. _____

H. _____

I. _____

11. What are the principles of study given in your text?

A. _____

B. _____

C _____

D. _____

E. _____

F. _____

12. One of the responsibilities of the Bible teacher is to make sure the Church is _____ and _____ in the truth.

13. Leaders study so they will not ashamed to have their work _____ by God.

14. Preachers and teachers must be certain that they are anchored in the word so that when severe trials come, they will show an _____ loyalty to the truth.

15. Copy II Timothy 5:17 _____

_____

_____

Journaling

Chapter Thirteen
What is My Ministry Fit?

Questions

1. Define vocational ministry.

   _____

   _____

   _____

   _____

   _____

2. Who in the Bible portrayed both vocational and bi-vocational ministry?

   _____

3. It is a requirement within some organizations that pastors be employed full-time because of the assigned work load. _____True _____False

4. Name ten of the common topics of catechism training.
   A. _____

   B. _____

   C. _____

   D. _____

   E. _____

   F. _____

   G. _____

   H. _____

   I. _____

   J. _____

5. _____ is a process by which individuals are consecrated or set apart as clergy to perform various Christian rites and ceremonies.

6. _____ that choose bi-vocational ministry over vocational ministry does so because it affords them with the opportunity to spend a significant amount of _____ with their flock while also having the freedom to do _____ endeavors beyond the walls of the church building.

7. No one will expect you to prove your calling. _____True _____False

8. A _____ is a tentative approval of the church to move forward in service until ordination.

9. _____ means to teach in an orderly and systematic way, by word of mouth, in the form of dialogue – question and answer.

10. Ask for a_____, if one is not assigned. This will give you the opportunity to see ministry at work first hand, and observe the positive effects of Christian virtues at work in the Christian life.

11. The person who is undergoing the process of ordination is called the

_____.

12. _____ must be initiated as a call along with an anointing from God, and the empowerment to do the work one is called to.

Journaling

Chapter Fourteen
An Example of Basic Catechism Questions

1. Explain justification and give your scripture basis.

2. What is water baptism?

3. How is water baptism to be administered?

4. Is there a biblical pattern of doctrine?

5. You are being catechized. Explain catechism.

6. Are there more Gods than one?

7. How did God create man?

8. What information does the Bible give concerning the birth of the New Testament Church?

9. Define sanctification.

10. What is sin?

11. What caused the fall of man?

12. Explain the doctrine of the trinity.

13. How does Christ perform the office of High Priest?

14. What steps did God take in order to be manifested among men?

15. What is the Lord's Supper?

16. How should the Lord's Supper be administered?

17. What is the duty that God requires of man?

18. What is the work of the Holy Spirit?

19. What is the Great Commission?

20. What event in the Bible do most theologians use as documented evidence of the birth of the New Testament Church?

21. What are the divisions of the Old Testament?

22. Name the divisions of the New Testament

23. At what point in his life was Moses commissioned to go to Egypt as Israel's leader?

24. What is the mission of the church?

25. What is purpose of prayer?

Journaling: Answer the catechism questions.

Chapter Fifteen
An Example of an Ordination Service

Presider or Worship Leader

Processional of Elders & Candidate

Musical Selection

Welcome

Statement of Purpose

New Testament Reading

Old Testament Reading

Musical Tribute

Acknowledgement of Candidate's Family

The Ordination Ceremony

Presentation of the Candidate

Examination of the Candidate

    Charge to the Candidate

    Charge to the Church

    Laying on of Hands

        (Prayer of Consecration)

    Presentation of License

Musical Tribute

Presentation of Tokens of Ministry

Presentation of Candidate

Closing Remarks

Benediction

Journaling: Fill in the Ordination Program.

Personal Readiness Post Test   (Answer using Y or N)

1. Are you a spirit-filled Christian?

2. Have you turned from all sin (repented) and promise to keep yourself clean and chaste before God? _____

3. Is it your earnest intention to align your life with the eternal purpose of your Heavenly Father? _____

4. Have you totally surrendered yourself to God and seek to obey His will at all costs? _____

5. Is your supreme goal to add to God's kingdom and build up the Church of Jesus Christ?__ _____

6. Will you sincerely pray for the Holy Spirit to lead and guide you in all you say and do? __ ____

7. Do you possess the passion **to serve** in any capacity where you are needed? _____

8. Are you willing to help and be a blessing to others as opportunities arise? _____

9. Are you devoted to meeting the spiritual needs of all people? _____

10. Are you willing to submit to the necessary Biblical training required by your local leadership and by God? _____

11. Do you see ministry as the privilege to serve others rather than a means of achieving social recognition and prestige? _____

12. Is the carrying out of the Great Commission your primary goal in ministry? _____

13. Are you committed to lifting up Christ, rather than your own name and

position? _____

14. Do you stand ready "instant in season and out of season" to preach the gospel and share the love of Christ to all people? _____

15. Are you willing to stand for what is right, though unpopular, and suffer shame for the Gospel? _____

16. Do you promise to provide leadership by your own example? _____

17. Do you have a mentor or coach? _____

18. Are you affiliated with a local church? _____

19. The Bible commands believers to "come ye out from among them and be ye separate." Will you disassociate yourself from any individual or group that persist in living in sin, or who does not hold the Bible as the authoritative Word of God? _____

20. Are you willing to submit to God's process for Christian growth and development? _____

Called to Serve: The Minister in the Making

A Roadmap to Ministerial Training Companion Workbook

Made in the USA
Columbia, SC
13 December 2024